Ants in the Park

Written by Ian MacDonald

Illustrated by Lucy Fleming

RISING ★ STARS

That man is on my nest!

Get him to jump up and run off!

"Yap! Yap!" went Dog to the man.

4

The man did not jump up. Not yet!

Rub! Rub! Rub! went Cat on the man.

The man still did not get up. Not yet!

"We quit!" yaps Dog.

Not yet!

A mass of ants ran from the nest.

Nip! Nip! Nip! Up his leg ran the ants.

"Help! Ants in my pants!" Off he ran!

Talk about the story

Ask your child these questions:

1 Who tried to make the man jump up first?

2 How did Cat try to make the man jump up?

3 How do you think the man felt about Cat and Dog?

4 What was Ant's plan? Did it work?

5 What would you do to make the man jump up?

6 Have you ever seen an ants' nest?

Can your child retell the story using their own words?